First published in Great Britain by Heinemann Library
Halley Court, Jordan Hill, Oxford OX2 8EJ
a division of Reed Educational & Professional Publishing Ltd

OXFORD FLORENCE PRAGUE MADRID ATHENS
MELBOURNE AUCKLAND KUALA LUMPUR SINGAPORE TOKYO
IBADAN NAIROBI KAMPALA JOHANNESBURG GABORONE
PORTSMOUTH NH CHICAGO MEXICO CITY SÃO PAULO

First edition © Éditions Mango 1995

This edition © Reed Educational and Professional Publishing Ltd 1997

Designed by Marion de Rouvray and Celia Floyd
Illustrations by Sophie de Seynes
Printed in France

01 00 99 98 97
10 9 8 7 6 5 4 3 2 1
ISBN 0 431 05438 X

British Library Cataloguing in Publication Data

Royer, Alain
    Water into wine. – (Bible stories)
    1. Bible stories, English – Juvenile literature
    I. Title II. Carpentier, Georges
    221.9 ' 505

Acknowledgements
Our thanks to Jan Thompson and Clare Boast for their comments in the preparation of this book.

Every effort has been made to contact copyright holders of any material reproduced in this
book. Any omissions will be rectified in subsequent printings if notice is given to the Publisher.

BIBLE STORIES

Water into Wine

Written by

Alain Royer and Georges Carpentier

Illustrated by

Sophie de Seynes

Heinemann

Jesus was about thirty years old when he left Nazareth. He had lived there with his parents. He made his way to the Sea of Galilee.

It was there that he called his first disciples. He noticed Simon and his brother Andrew, throwing their nets into the sea. They were fishermen, like many of the people in that area.

Jesus said to them, 'Come with me. You will no longer load your boat with fish, but with people.' Simon and Andrew left their nets and followed him.

A little later, Jesus saw James and his
brother John. They were fishermen, too. They
were at sea with their father and his servants.
Jesus called James and John to him, and they
followed him.

Jesus went on his way and came to Cana, a town in Galilee. On that day, there was a big wedding feast. Jesus's mother Mary was there. Jesus and his disciples were invited, too.

During the feast, Mary saw that the wine jars were empty. She whispered to her son, 'They have run out of wine. Do something to help.' At first Jesus would not do anything, but then he agreed.

Mary told the servants, 'What my son asks for may surprise you. Even so, do as he tells you.'

There were six large empty jars in the hall. Jesus said to the servants, 'Fill these jars with water.' The servants did as he told them.

ST. MARY'S COLLEGE
FALLS ROAD, BELFAST 12.

Then Jesus said to the servants, 'Fill a glass from one of these jars. Then take it to the head waiter for him to taste.'

When the head waiter took a sip from the glass, the water had turned into wine. But he was not surprised by this. He did not know that the servants had poured water into the jars, and that Jesus had turned that water into wine.

The head waiter went to the bridegroom and said to him, 'Sir, most people serve the best wine first, and the poorer wine later. But you have saved the best wine until now.'

This is how Jesus first showed people that he was sent by God. His disciples believed in him, and went with him when he left the wedding feast.